Yeats, William Butler, 1865–1939. ✓690042
 Running to paradise; an introductory selection by Kevin
Crossley-Holland. Illustrated by Judith Valpy. New
York, Macmillan [°1967]

  93 p. illus. 22 cm.

  Poems.

  I. Crossley-Holland, Kevin, ed. II. Title.

RUNNING TO PARADISE

RUNNING TO PARADISE

W. B. YEATS

AN INTRODUCTORY SELECTION BY
KEVIN CROSSLEY-HOLLAND

ILLUSTRATED BY
JUDITH VALPY

THE MACMILLAN COMPANY
NEW YORK

I call on those that call me son,
Grandson, or great-grandson,
On uncles, aunts, great uncles or great aunts,
To judge what I have done.

Are you Content?

The Soul.   Seek out reality, leave things that seem.
The Heart.   What, be a singer born and lack a theme?

Vacillation

CONTENTS

Introduction   9

The Indian upon God   27
The Stolen Child   28
To an Isle in the Water   31
A Faery Song   32
The Lake Isle of Innisfree   33
When You are Old   34
The Ballad of Father Gilligan   35
The Lover tells of the Rose in his Heart   37
The Host of the Air   38
The Song of Wandering Aengus   41
The Song of the Old Mother   42
He remembers Forgotten Beauty   43
The Cap and Bells   44
He wishes for the Cloths of Heaven   46
The Fiddler of Dooney   47
Adam's Curse   48
Red Hanrahan's Song about Ireland   51
The Old Men Admiring Themselves in the Water   52
To a Poet, who would have me Praise certain Bad   53
    Poets, Imitators of His and Mine

Brown Penny   53
September 1913   54
Running to Paradise   56
To a Child Dancing in the Wind   59
Two Years Later   59
An Appointment   61
A Coat   62
The Wild Swans at Coole   63
An Irish Airman Foresees his Death   66
A Song   67
The Scholars   68
The Fisherman   69
Memory   71
The Cat and the Moon   71
The Rose Tree   73
To be Carved on a Stone at Thoor Ballylee   74
For Anne Gregory   75
A Prayer for Old Age   76
The Wicked Hawthorn Tree   77
From Supernatural Songs   78
What Then?   79
The Ghost of Roger Casement   81
Come Gather Round Me, Parnellites   83
Three Songs to the One Burden : III   85
Why should not Old Men be Mad?   87
The Statesman's Holiday   88
Politics   90
From Under Ben Bulben   91
Index of First Lines   93

INTRODUCTION

FEW people change very much ; some, like W. B. Yeats, change barely at all. As he grew up and grew old, Yeats acquired new interests, of course, and continually developed both as man and writer ; and as the world changed about him, moving out of the nineteenth century and into the twentieth, he half-heartedly attempted to adapt himself to it. But what is partly true of everyone was largely true of Yeats : his inheritance and his boyhood experiences remained with him always.

Much of the poetry Yeats wrote was about himself — a graph of his own journey through this world. Because that is so, it is well worth knowing a few facts about his life. The point of this introduction is to give you some of those facts, particularly about his childhood, and to show how they shaped some of his poems.

William Butler Yeats was born on 13 June 1865. His mother and father both came from County Sligo in the west of Ireland ; but he was only one when his father decided to give up law and concentrate on being a painter. The family then moved to London, very much more a centre for art and artists than anywhere in Ireland. And there it grew with the birth of four further children, the best known of whom was Jack, who later became the greatest painter of his time; many were the occasions on which he sketched Willy, as everyone called him, 'his dark face, its touch of vivid colouring, the night black hair, the eager dark eyes'.

So for the first fifteen years of his life Willy shunted to and fro between London and Sligo. In term-time he was taught first by his father, then later he went to the Godolphin School at Hammersmith. His holidays were spent in Sligo, sometimes with and sometimes without his parents, usually at the house of his grandfather, William Pollexfen.

But if Willy's time was divided, his loyalties were not; he was of Sligo and for Sligo. He was there always, in mind if not in body, and boasted to his friends of the romantic voyage to the west coast of Ireland : 'the look of the great cliffs of Donegal, and Tory island men coming alongside with lobsters, talking Irish and, if it was night, blowing on a burning sod to draw our attention'.

Although Willy looked forward to his holidays, he was alarmed by his grandfather. 'He had a violent temper and kept a hatchet at his bedside for burglars and would knock a man down instead of going to law, and I once saw him hunt a party of men with a horsewhip.' But then, as a boy, Willy was alarmed easily ; if he had some cause to fear his tough, proud old grandfather, it was aggravated by his own shyness and sensitivity. His grandmother, on the other hand, was a gentle and patient woman, though perhaps rather self-righteous ; certainly, Willy's mother took after her rather than William Pollexfen.

It was when Willy was left to his own devices and began to roam over the Sligo countryside that his spirits soared. He had a red pony of his own, he went sailing with the local coastguard ; above all he liked to climb the bald mountains, to fish in the clear streams :

> Where the wandering water gushes
> From the hills above Glen-Car
> In pools among the rushes
> That scarce could bathe a star,
> We seek for slumbering trout
> And whispering in their ears
> Give them unquiet dreams;

Willy came to love the Sligo countryside, presided over by the great bare mountain Ben Bulben, more and more deeply as the years passed ; and not less so for being absent from it for most of the time. In old age he remembered how as a boy in London, 'I longed for a sod of earth from some field I knew, something of Sligo to hold in my hand'.

Yeats's great love for Sligo, developed in those short holidays a hundred years ago, remained with him for the rest of his life. It wells up again and again in his work. In this book you will come across the sands of Rosses Point near Sligo town ; Cummen Strand ; Innisfree, the wooded island in Lough Gill, opposite Slish Wood ; Castle Dargan, a ruin overlooking a lake, near which Willy fished for pike ; and village names full of music —

Drumcliff, Dooney, Knocknarea, Kilvarnet, Mocharabuiee.

During his holidays in Sligo Willy also met other relatives, his uncles and aunts and cousins : Yeatses, respected and respectable but rather decayed, full of family history, scornful of the Pollexfens for caring so much about money ; Pollexfens, well-off and always concerned with 'making a living', arrogant but hospitable ; and Middletons, relatives of Willy's mother, traders, practical people, lacking in ambition or pride, good friends to the country folk round about them. And it was while staying with his great uncle William Middleton, whose house had once belonged to a smuggler, that Willy heard many more of those Irish stories for which his mother had already whetted his appetite, homesick in London. He heard them from local people in the cottages near by, people like Paddy Flynn, 'a little bright-eyed old man, living in a leaky one-roomed cottage of the village of Ballisodare'. These stories, about the little folk, about headless women, shadow hares, fire-tongued hounds and whistling seals, and about the heroes and heroines of Irish mythology, seized Willy's imagination as nothing had done before.

You can see how later they influenced his work from poems in this book like 'The Stolen Child', 'A Faery Song', 'Red Hanrahan's Song about Ireland', 'The Wicked Hawthorn Tree', and the haunting vision of O'Driscoll in 'The Host of the Air' :

> He heard while he sang and dreamed
> A piper piping away,

And never was piping so sad,
And never was piping so gay.

And he saw young men and young girls
Who danced on a level place,
And Bridget his bride among them,
With a sad and a gay face.

In middle age Yeats saw how his 'fleas', as he arrogantly called his inferior imitators, were debasing the same material he had used so brilliantly, and he angrily wrote 'The Coat'. For the truth is that these stories, which seemed to the boy like a way of escape from the loneliness of this world, had become in the hands of the man one way of reasserting the greatness and the individuality of Ireland.

It was magic, in particular, that had such an intense effect upon Willy. He began to see, or imagine he saw, magic things himself; but he would only turn it all into a joke if he was asked about it, for he was unsure of himself and afraid that people would only laugh at him.

Yeats never lost his interest in magic : it seemed to him a key to understanding the meaning of life. Rejecting Christianity, he became associated in his twenties with people and societies interested in mysticism, the supernatural, spiritualism, magic, and throughout his life searched restlessly for some system that would help him to find truth. Inevitably, this influenced many of his poems ; but, great poet that he was, Yeats wrote on different levels at the same time with extraordinary transparency. You can read and enjoy most of those poems which are based on his complete theories (which he expounded in his prose work, *A Vision*) without having to grasp the theories themselves.

Yeats did not come by his transparency easily. The clarity and magical incantation which are so much part of his style, particularly in his earlier and later poems, were acquired by hard work no less than by vision. He was a master craftsman, and it is not until you scrutinise his poems closely that his immense subtlety becomes apparent. Yeats believed all poetry should be spoken, not read; and in his case it is certainly true that only by listening will you fully discover his spell; for the greatness of Yeats (and, oddly enough, he was tone deaf) lies as much in sound as in meaning.

Back to London. To begin with, Willy was taught by his father, who, although he had firm ideas about education, was by no means cut out for the job. All too often he frightened his son, who was very slow to learn to read. And yet you can judge how well he understood Willy from part of a letter he wrote to his wife: 'I am very anxious about Willy, he is never out of my thoughts. I believe him to be intensely affectionate, but from shyness, sensitiveness and nervousness, difficult to win and yet he is worth winning. I should of course like to see him do what is right, but he will only develop by kindness and affection and gentleness.'

All the same, schooling from his father must have seemed enjoyable to Willy by comparison with the

Godolphin School, Hammersmith, 'a Gothic building of yellow brick', to which he was sent when he was ten. From the first day to the last he hated it. He had never before come into day-to-day contact with boys of his own age, and he found that he did not make friends easily. He was an outsider, too, an Irish boy amongst the English. How the Black Prince gained his spurs at Crécy, how Nelson lost his life but won the day at Trafalgar meant nothing to him.

Willy was certainly no weakling; he learned to box (mainly for self-defence) and to swim excellently. Yet for all that he was often bullied; and he was hardly helped by an Irish master who reprimanded him for being idle, saying that one Irish boy was cleverer than a class-room of English boys; 'a description', wrote Yeats, 'I had to pay for afterwards'.

All things considered, it is not surprising that Willy was quick to develop a dislike of the English character just as great as his liking for the Irish. The two were in-dissoluble, and they remained so for the rest of his life. For although the poet Yeats wrote in English, married an English girl, and counted many English amongst his friends, he bitterly resented the English domination of Ireland, and was deeply involved in the Irish nationalist movement.

He used the stories he had heard in Sligo in an attempt to re-create an heroic Ireland; he founded the Irish National Dramatic Theatre; he was the unquestioned leader of the Anglo-Irish literary revival that included

15

amongst its numbers J. M. Synge, Æ, Lady Gregory and many others ; he worked hard to try to reunite different nationalist groups in Ireland ; he was for a while member of the secret Irish Republican Brotherhood. Yet he was filled with a growing sense of helplessness by the endless talk about an Independent Ireland and despised the revolutionaries for their complete lack of action ; and when the civil Uprising finally came, in Easter 1916, Yeats was taken completely by surprise. Now that men had acted, now that blood had been shed, he changed his tune, considering

> All changed, changed utterly:
> A terrible beauty is born.

In this book, you will meet the Fenian leader O'Leary, who had a great influence on Yeats ; and you will meet the revolutionaries, Pearse, Connolly, and Roger Casement, who was hanged by the English for being a traitor. Above all, you will meet Parnell, the great Irishman whose natural death in 1892 was the direct cause of this prolonged outburst of national feeling :

> He fought the might of England
> And saved the Irish poor
> Whatever good a farmer's got
> He brought it all to pass.

But Yeats as politician was really only concerned with matters concerning Ireland. Later in his life he served a term in the Senate and made provocative speeches there, but half the time he was angry at being so powerless, and he did not bother to seek re-election. In 'An Appointment' he records his feelings about 'Being out of heart with government' very precisely.

Yeats's great sense of responsibility to Ireland, then, and his attitude towards England, may be traced back, in part at least, to his love-longing for Sligo, his experiences at the Godolphin School. And it was during his years at that school, too, that he began to sense he was somehow separate, different. Later he was to write :

> His chosen comrades thought at school
> He must grow a famous man;
> He thought the same. . . .

This sense helps to explain why, despite periods of happiness, despite brothers and sisters who perhaps meant more to him in later life, he was essentially lonely as a boy. When he was fifty he wrote, 'I remember little of childhood but its pain'.

The sense of being separate, like so many other elements of his childhood, remained with Yeats. He came to believe, in his father's words, that 'the poet is always solitary' and must therefore be no stranger to loneliness. In 1917 he bought for thirty-five pounds a tower, an old square castle at Ballylee in Galway that had caught his eye some years before. Yeats had it restored and used it as a summer home (it was too damp in winter) ; but he also used it in his poetry as a symbol of his detachment, his search in solitude for wisdom ; and it was there that he wrote his greatest poems.

When Willy was fifteen his family returned to Ireland,

to Howth just outside Dublin, and he was sent to Dublin High School. The contrast with Godolphin could hardly have been more marked : it was a rough-and-tumble place ; there was forever a din of voices ; 'cricket and football, the collecting of moths and butterflies, though not forbidden, were discouraged' ; the emphasis fell squarely on hard work.

This did not suit Willy at all. He was no less idle, if rather more happy, at Dublin High School than at Godolphin, only bothering when a subject really caught his interest. When he did bother he excelled, for he was in fact extremely clever. It was, above all, natural history that preoccupied him at this time ; literature was his worst subject.

Willy's father, moreover, was always poking a finger in the pie. He frequently reinforced Willy's knowledge of Latin when his son should have been doing 'prep' in some other subject, making sweeping pronouncements like 'Geography should never be taught. It is not a training for the mind.' Later, Yeats came to agree with his father's ideas about education : 'All he said was, I now believe, right, but he should have taken me away from school. He would have taught me nothing but Greek and Latin, and I would now be an educated man.'

Willy's gentle, unassuming mother, who never read a book and never looked at pictures, who loved nothing so much as to talk to fishermen and their wives, influenced her son in many ways, not least in fostering his love of Sligo. But just as William Pollexfen had occupied the centre of the stage for the first ten years of Willy's life, his father did so now.

J. B. Yeats had a studio in Dublin and he and Willy used to travel by train and breakfast there each morning, before Willy proceeded to school. J. B. Yeats was a Pre-Raphaelite painter, a member of the movement who believed in 'simplicity and accuracy of detail, in freshness and directness and precision, and looked to medieval work to find them'. He had the same ideas about literature and thought Victorian poetry artificial and choked with ideas. When he and Willy discussed poetry he would praise above all the dramatic element and declaim passionate moments from dramatic poems.

Willy certainly inherited much of his father's dramatic sense. He wrote verse plays throughout his life ; and though they must take second place to his poetry, many of them are of a very high order, such as *The Countess Cathleen*. But perhaps Yeats's greatest contribution to drama was to found in 1904, in conjunction with Lady Gregory, the Abbey Theatre in Dublin ; to manage it for six years ; and to discover, stage there and defend works of genius such as J. M. Synge's *The Playboy of the Western World*. The Abbey Theatre was the very centre of the Irish literary revival ; and Yeats was at the centre of the Abbey Theatre.

But long before those studio breakfasts in 1881 Willy had heard his father read poetry aloud. At the age of eight or nine he had sat with him under the acres of sky on the tongue of land between Sligo and Rosses Point, and listened to the *Lays of Ancient Rome, Ivanhoe* and *The Lay of the Last Minstrel*. In old age Yeats remembered those occasions vividly. And he remembered, too, his first experience of poetry, shared with his grandfather's stable boy, at that time his best friend: 'He had a book of Orange rhymes, and the days when we read them together in the hayloft gave me the pleasure of rhyme for the first time.'

So it was that, at the age of sixteen — boyhood's end — Willy began to write poems and verse plays. They were heavily influenced by his father's ideas, by Spenser and by Shelley; often lines did not scan. But the great spring in him had surfaced; it was fresh and transparent and full of energy; nothing was going to stop it.

There are, of course, themes in Yeats's poetry which his boyhood experiences did not anticipate and, indeed, could not have anticipated. Two, in particular, occur in this book.

Yeats was twenty-three when he first met Maud Gonne. 'Her complexion was luminous, like that of apple blossom through which the light falls, and I remember her standing that first day by a great heap of such blossoms in the window.' Maud Gonne was outstandingly beautiful, of great height, like himself a fervent nationalist, a woman of eloquence and energy and action. To Yeats she seemed the incarnation of the heroic spirit of Ireland. 'In the next few years I saw her always when she passed to and fro between Dublin and Paris, surrounded, no matter how rapid the journey and how brief her stay at either end of it, by cages full of birds, canaries, finches of all kinds, dogs, a parrot, and once a full grown hawk from Donegal.'

Yeats fell in love with her. For a time he was too shy to tell her ; and when, at the age of twenty-six, he brought himself to do so, she rejected him. She was to do so again many times, and yet for all that she liked him, and at times needed him. They remained very close friends until 1903, when Maud Gonne deeply hurt Yeats by suddenly marrying another man ; and when that man died Yeats was back on the doorstep again until, in 1917, he married and married happily an English girl whom he had known for a number of years, George Hyde-Lees.

Out of his seemingly endless, hopeless love for Maud Gonne, Yeats was impelled to write the greatest love-poems of the age. You will find some of them here, solemn and sad and stately : 'The Lover tells of the Rose in his Heart', 'He wishes for the Cloths of Heaven' and 'He remembers Forgotten Beauty' :

> When my arms wrap you round I press
> My heart upon the loveliness
> That has long faded from the world;

Many of Yeats's finest love-poems were included in his third collection of poetry, *The Wind Amongst the Reeds*, which was published in 1899. But not without difficulty : a reader at the House of Macmillan, which ultimately and perhaps undeservedly became Yeats's publisher despite rejecting this book, reported : 'The work does not please the ear, nor kindle the imagination, nor hint a thought for one's reflection . . . I do not say it is obscure, or uncouth or barbaric or affected — tho' it is all these evil things. I say it is to me absolute *nullity.'* Time mocks those words. But Yeats's love-poems speak of timeless emotion and values ; the irony is that if Maud Gonne had made Yeats happy he would not have had to write them.

Another theme which increasingly occupied Yeats was old age. This is the subject of 'The Wild Swans at Coole' in which Yeats laments the passing of time, and envies the seemingly constant swans :

> Their hearts have not grown old;
> Passion or conquest, wander where they will,
> Attend upon them still.

Yeats had barely anticipated that after his time of flames there would be a time of embers. Who does ?

> O who could have foretold
> That the heart grows old?

In many of his later poems Yeats laments for his lost youth, his lost love. In truth, he was lamenting a lost world too — a dignified world of rigidly defined orders, of aristocracy and peasants, a world he had outlived.

In his youth Yeats had often spent whole summers at Coole Park, in Galway, the home of Lady Gregory. And he wrote that he had found there 'what I had been seeking always, a life of order, and of labour, where all outward things were in the image of an inward life . . . here many generations, and no uncultured generations, had left the images of this service in furniture, in statues, in pictures and in the outline of wood and field'. Now, revisiting Coole Park in old age, shortly before Lady Gregory's death and before it fell into disrepair, he made it a symbol of that lost world :

> We were the last romantics — chose for theme
> Traditional sanctity and loveliness;
> Whatever's written in what poets name
> The book of the people; whatever most can bless
> The mind of man or elevate a rhyme;
> But all is changed, that high horse riderless,
> Though mounted in that saddle Homer rode
> Where the swan drifts upon a darkening flood.

Yeats was, indeed, the last great Romantic, and the changing face of the world about him, drifting towards a Second World War, filled him with bitterness and pride :

> Scorn the sort now growing up
> All out of shape from toe to top.

Increasingly he turned back to think about his friends ; and no poet in the English language has written more movingly about friendship :

> Think where man's glory most begins and ends,
> And say my glory was I had such friends.

Above all Yeats continued to reassert again and again the values in which he so passionately believed, his already lost world :

> Cast your mind on other days
> That we in coming days may be
> Still the indomitable Irishry.

When Yeats was seventy-four he foresaw, as other poets have before him, his own death. And in the South of France, where he had been sent by his doctors, his mind turned more strongly than ever to Sligo. He wrote about it, arranged that he should be buried there, and coined himself an epitaph,

Cast a cold eye
On life, on death.
Horseman, pass by!

But that is one thing Yeats did not have, 'a cold eye'. It is only what he wanted to have. He was in fact a warm, involved man, an actor as well as recorder of the events of his age. And his achievement was such that this great poet — the only English-speaking poet of this century whose greatness is beyond question — made that age his own.

This selection attempts to present as many aspects of Yeats's poetry as possible and to balance the phases of his development. It is the first to have been made and published with children in mind. My wife, my father, and a few friends, especially Dorothea Stuart, have been very kind in helping to shape it; Judith Valpy has drawn fine illustrations for it; above all, Mrs. George Yeats and Mr. Michael Butler Yeats have been most generous in giving their blessing to it.

4 *May* 1967   Kevin Crossley-Holland

RUNNING TO PARADISE

The Indian upon God

I PASSED along the water's edge below the humid trees,
My spirit rocked in evening light, the rushes round my
    knees,
My spirit rocked in sleep and sighs ; and saw the moor-
    fowl pace
All dripping on a grassy slope, and saw them cease to
    chase
Each other round in circles, and heard the eldest speak :
Who holds the world between His bill and made us strong or
    weak
Is an undying moorfowl, and He lives beyond the sky.
The rains are from His dripping wing, the moonbeams from
    His eye.
I passed a little further on and heard a lotus talk :
Who made the world and ruleth it, He hangeth on a stalk,
For I am in His image made, and all this tinkling tide
Is but a sliding drop of rain between His petals wide.
A little way within the gloom a roebuck raised his eyes
Brimful of starlight, and he said : *The Stamper of the*
    Skies,
He is a gentle roebuck; for how else, I pray, could He
Conceive a thing so sad and soft, a gentle thing like me ?
I passed a little further on and heard a peacock say :
Who made the grass and made the worms and made my
    feathers gay,
He is a monstrous peacock, and He waveth all the night
His languid tail above us, lit with myriad spots of light.

27

The Stolen Child

WHERE dips the rocky highland
Of Sleuth Wood in the lake,
There lies a leafy island
Where flapping herons wake
The drowsy water-rats ;
There we've hid our faery vats,
Full of berries
And of reddest stolen cherries.
Come away, O human child !
To the waters and the wild

With a faery, hand in hand,
For the world's more full of weeping than you
    can understand.

Where the wave of moonlight glosses
The dim grey sands with light,
Far off by furthest Rosses
We foot it all the night,
Weaving olden dances,
Mingling hands and mingling glances
Till the moon has taken flight ;
To and fro we leap
And chase the frothy bubbles,
While the world is full of troubles
And is anxious in its sleep.
Come away, O human child !
To the waters and the wild
With a faery, hand in hand,
For the world's more full of weeping than you
    can understand.

Where the wandering water gushes
From the hills above Glen-Car,
In pools among the rushes
That scarce could bathe a star,
We seek for slumbering trout
And whispering in their ears
Give them unquiet dreams ;
Leaning softly out

From ferns that drop their tears
Over the young streams.
Come away, O human child!
To the waters and the wild
With a faery, hand in hand,
For the world's more full of weeping than you
*   can understand.*

Away with us he's going,
The solemn-eyed :
He'll hear no more the lowing
Of the calves on the warm hillside
Or the kettle on the hob.
Sing peace into his breast,
Or see the brown mice bob
Round and round the oatmeal-chest.
For he comes, the human child,
To the waters and the wild
With a faery, hand in hand,
From a world more full of weeping than he
*   can understand.*

To an Isle in the Water

SHY one, shy one,
Shy one of my heart,
She moves in the firelight
Pensively apart.

She carries in the dishes,
And lays them in a row.
To an isle in the water
With her would I go.

She carries in the candles,
And lights the curtained room,
Shy in the doorway
And shy in the gloom ;

And shy as a rabbit,
Helpful and shy.
To an isle in the water
With her would I fly.

A Faery Song

Sung by the people of Faery over Diarmuid and
Grania, in their bridal sleep under a Cromlech

WE who are old, old and gay,
O so old !
Thousands of years, thousands of years,
If all were told:

Give to these children, new from the world,
Silence and love ;
And the long dew-dropping hours of the night,
And the stars above :

Give to these children, new from the world,
Rest far from men.
Is anything better, anything better ?
Tell us it then :

Us who are old, old and gay,
O so old !
Thousands of years, thousands of years,
If all were told.

The Lake Isle of Innisfree

I WILL arise and go now, and go to Innisfree,
And a small cabin build there, of clay and wattles made :
Nine bean-rows will I have there, a hive for the honey-
    bee,
And live alone in the bee-loud glade.

And I shall have some peace there, for peace comes
    dropping slow,
Dropping from the veils of the morning to where the
    cricket sings ;
There midnight's all a glimmer, and noon a purple
    glow,
And evening full of the linnet's wings.

I will arise and go now, for always night and day
I hear lake water lapping with low sounds by the shore ;
While I stand on the roadway, or on the pavements
    grey,
I hear it in the deep heart's core.

When You are Old

WHEN you are old and grey and full of sleep,
And nodding by the fire, take down this book,
And slowly read, and dream of the soft look
Your eyes had once, and of their shadows deep ;

How many loved your moments of glad grace,
And loved your beauty with love false or true,
But one man loved the pilgrim soul in you,
And loved the sorrows of your changing face ;

And bending down beside the glowing bars,
Murmur, a little sadly, how Love fled
And paced upon the mountains overhead
And hid his face amid a crowd of stars.

The Ballad of Father Gilligan

THE old priest Peter Gilligan
Was weary night and day ;
For half his flock were in their beds,
Or under green sods lay.

Once, while he nodded on a chair,
At the moth-hour of eve,
Another poor man sent for him,
And he began to grieve.

'I have no rest, nor joy, nor peace,
For people die and die' ;
And after cried he, 'God forgive !
My body spake, not I !'

He knelt, and leaning on the chair
He prayed and fell asleep ;
And the moth-hour went from the fields,
And stars began to peep.

They slowly into millions grew,
And leaves shook in the wind ;
And God covered the world with shade,
And whispered to mankind.

Upon the time of sparrow-chirp
When the moths came once more,

The old priest Peter Gilligan
Stood upright on the floor.

'Mavrone, mavrone! the man has died
While I slept on the chair';
He roused his horse out of its sleep,
And rode with little care.

He rode now as he never rode,
By rocky lane and fen;
The sick man's wife opened the door:
'Father! you come again!'

'And is the poor man dead?' he cried.
'He died an hour ago.'
The old priest Peter Gilligan
In grief swayed to and fro.

'When you were gone, he turned and died
As merry as a bird.'
The old priest Peter Gilligan
He knelt him at that word.

'He Who hath made the night of stars
For souls who tire and bleed,
Sent one of His great angels down
To help me in my need.

'He Who is wrapped in purple robes,
With planets in His care,
Had pity on the least of things
Asleep upon a chair.'

The Lover tells of the Rose in his Heart

ALL things uncomely and broken, all things worn out
  and old,
The cry of a child by the roadway, the creak of a lumber-
  ing cart,
The heavy steps of the ploughman, splashing the wintry
  mould,
Are wronging your image that blossoms a rose in the
  deeps of my heart.

The wrong of unshapely things is a wrong too great
  to be told ;
I hunger to build them anew and sit on a green knoll
  apart,
With the earth and the sky and the water, remade, like
  a casket of gold
For my dreams of your image that blossoms a rose in
  the deeps of my heart.

The Host of the Air

O'DRISCOLL drove with a song
The wild duck and the drake
From the tall and the tufted reeds
Of the drear Hart Lake.

And he saw how the reeds grew dark
At the coming of night-tide,
And dreamed of the long dim hair
Of Bridget his bride.

He heard while he sang and dreamed
A piper piping away,
And never was piping so sad,
And never was piping so gay.

And he saw young men and young girls
Who danced on a level place,
And Bridget his bride among them,
With a sad and a gay face.

The dancers crowded about him
And many a sweet thing said,
And a young man brought him red wine
And a young girl white bread.

But Bridget drew him by the sleeve
Away from the merry bands,
To old men playing at cards
With a twinkling of ancient hands.

The bread and the wine had a doom,
For these were the host of the air ;
He sat and played in a dream
Of her long dim hair.

He played with the merry old men
And thought not of evil chance,
Until one bore Bridget his bride
Away from the merry dance.

He bore her away in his arms,
The handsomest young man there,
And his neck and his breast and his arms
Were drowned in her long dim hair.

O'Driscoll scattered the cards
And out of his dream awoke :
Old men and young men and young girls
Were gone like a drifting smoke ;

But he heard high up in the air
A piper piping away,
And never was piping so sad,
And never was piping so gay.

The Song of Wandering Aengus

I WENT out to the hazel wood,
Because a fire was in my head,
And cut and peeled a hazel wand,
And hooked a berry to a thread ;
And when white moths were on the wing,
And moth-like stars were flickering out,
I dropped the berry in a stream
And caught a little silver trout.

When I had laid it on the floor
I went to blow the fire aflame,
But something rustled on the floor,
And some one called me by my name :
It had become a glimmering girl
With apple blossom in her hair
Who called me by my name and ran
And faded through the brightening air.

Though I am old with wandering
Through hollow lands and hilly lands,
I will find out where she has gone,
And kiss her lips and take her hands ;
And walk among long dappled grass,
And pluck till time and times are done
The silver apples of the moon,
The golden apples of the sun.

The Song of the Old Mother

I RISE in the dawn, and I kneel and blow
Till the seed of the fire flicker and glow ;
And then I must scrub and bake and sweep
Till stars are beginning to blink and peep ;
And the young lie long and dream in their bed
Of the matching of ribbons for bosom and head,
And their day goes over in idleness,
And they sigh if the wind but lift a tress :
While I must work because I am old,
And the seed of the fire gets feeble and cold.

He remembers Forgotten Beauty

When my arms wrap you round I press
My heart upon the loveliness
That has long faded from the world ;
The jewelled crowns that kings have hurled
In shadowy pools, when armies fled ;
The love-tales wrought with silken thread
By dreaming ladies upon cloth
That has made fat the murderous moth ;
The roses that of old time were
Woven by ladies in their hair,
The dew-cold lilies ladies bore
Through many a sacred corridor
Where such grey clouds of incense rose
That only God's eyes did not close :
For that pale breast and lingering hand
Come from a more dream-heavy land,
A more dream-heavy hour than this ;
And when you sigh from kiss to kiss
I hear white Beauty sighing, too,
For hours when all must fade like dew,
But flame on flame, and deep on deep,
Throne over throne where in half sleep,
Their swords upon their iron knees,
Brood her high lonely mysteries.

The Cap and Bells

THE jester walked in the garden :
The garden had fallen still ;
He bade his soul rise upward
And stand on her window-sill.

It rose in a straight blue garment,
When owls began to call :
It had grown wise-tongued by thinking
Of a quiet and light footfall ;

But the young queen would not listen ;
She rose in her pale night-gown ;
She drew in the heavy casement
And pushed the latches down.

He bade his heart go to her,
When the owls called out no more ;
In a red and quivering garment
It sang to her through the door.

It had grown sweet-tongued by dreaming
Of a flutter of flower-like hair ;
But she took up her fan from the table
And waved it off on the air.

'I have cap and bells,' he pondered,
'I will send them to her and die' ;

And when the morning whitened
He left them where she went by.

She laid them upon her bosom,
Under a cloud of her hair,
And her red lips sang them a love-song
Till stars grew out of the air.

She opened her door and her window,
And the heart and the soul came through,
To her right hand came the red one,
To her left hand came the blue.

They set up a noise like crickets,
A chattering wise and sweet,
And her hair was a folded flower
And the quiet of love in her feet.

He wishes for the Cloths of Heaven

HAD I the heavens' embroidered cloths,
Enwrought with golden and silver light,
The blue and the dim and the dark cloths
Of night and light and the half-light,
I would spread the cloths under your feet :
But I, being poor, have only my dreams ;
I have spread my dreams under your feet ;
Tread softly because you tread on my dreams.

The Fiddler of Dooney

WHEN I play on my fiddle in Dooney,
Folk dance like a wave of the sea ;
My cousin is priest in Kilvarnet,
My brother in Mocharabuiee.

I passed my brother and cousin :
They read in their books of prayer ;
I read in my book of songs
I bought at the Sligo fair.

When we come at the end of time
To Peter sitting in state,
He will smile on the three old spirits,
But call me first through the gate ;

For the good are always the merry,
Save by an evil chance,
And the merry love the fiddle,
And the merry love to dance :

And when the folk there spy me,
They will all come up to me,
With 'Here is the fiddler of Dooney !'
And dance like a wave of the sea.

Adam's Curse

WE sat together at one summer's end,
That beautiful mild woman, your close friend,
And you and I, and talked of poetry.
I said, 'A line will take us hours maybe ;
Yet if it does not seem a moment's thought,
Our stitching and unstitching has been naught.
Better go down upon your marrow-bones
And scrub a kitchen pavement, or break stones
Like an old pauper, in all kinds of weather ;
For to articulate sweet sounds together
Is to work harder than all these, and yet
Be thought an idler by the noisy set
Of bankers, schoolmasters, and clergymen
The martyrs call the world.'

                    And thereupon
That beautiful mild woman for whose sake
There's many a one shall find out all heartache
On finding that her voice is sweet and low
Replied, 'To be born woman is to know—
Although they do not talk of it at school—
That we must labour to be beautiful.'

I said, 'It's certain there is no fine thing
Since Adam's fall but needs much labouring.
There have been lovers who thought love should be
So much compounded of high courtesy

48

That they would sigh and quote with learned looks
Precedents out of beautiful old books ;
Yet now it seems an idle trade enough.'

We sat grown quiet at the name of love ;
We saw the last embers of daylight die,
And in the trembling blue-green of the sky
A moon, worn as if it had been a shell
Washed by time's waters as they rose and fell
About the stars and broke in days and years.

I had a thought for no one's but your ears :
That you were beautiful, and that I strove
To love you in the old high way of love ;
That it had all seemed happy, and yet we'd grown
As weary-hearted as that hollow moon.

Red Hanrahan's Song about Ireland

THE old brown thorn-trees break in two high over
    Cummen Strand,
Under a bitter black wind that blows from the left
    hand ;
Our courage breaks like an old tree in a black wind and
    dies,
But we have hidden in our hearts the flame out of the
    eyes
Of Cathleen, the daughter of Houlihan.

The wind has bundled up the clouds high over Knock-
    narea,
And thrown the thunder on the stones for all that
    Maeve can say.
Angers that are like noisy clouds have set our hearts
    abeat ;
But we have all bent low and low and kissed the quiet
    feet
Of Cathleen, the daughter of Houlihan.

The yellow pool has overflowed high up on Clooth-
    na-Bare,
For the wet winds are blowing out of the clinging air ;
Like heavy flooded waters our bodies and our blood ;
But purer than a tall candle before the Holy Rood
Is Cathleen, the daughter of Houlihan.

The Old Men Admiring Themselves in the Water

I HEARD the old, old men say,
'Everything alters,
And one by one we drop away.'
They had hands like claws, and their knees
Were twisted like the old thorn-trees
By the waters.
I heard the old, old men say,
'All that's beautiful drifts away
Like the waters.'

To a Poet, who would have me Praise certain Bad Poets, Imitators of His and Mine

You say, as I have often given tongue
In praise of what another's said or sung,
'Twere politic to do the like by these ;
But was there ever dog that praised his fleas ?

Brown Penny

I WHISPERED, 'I am too young.'
And then, 'I am old enough' ;
Wherefore I threw a penny
To find out if I might love.
'Go and love, go and love, young man,
If the lady be young and fair.'
Ah, penny, brown penny, brown penny,
I am looped in the loops of her hair.

O love is the crooked thing,
There is nobody wise enough
To find out all that is in it,
For he would be thinking of love
Till the stars had run away
And the shadows eaten the moon.
Ah, penny, brown penny, brown penny,
One cannot begin it too soon.

September 1913

WHAT need you, being come to sense,
But fumble in a greasy till
And add the halfpence to the pence
And prayer to shivering prayer, until
You have dried the marrow from the bone ?
For men were born to pray and save :
Romantic Ireland's dead and gone,
It's with O'Leary in the grave.

Yet they were of a different kind,
The names that stilled your childish play,
They have gone about the world like wind,
But little time had they to pray
For whom the hangman's rope was spun,
And what, God help us, could they save ?
Romantic Ireland's dead and gone,
It's with O'Leary in the grave.

Was it for this the wild geese spread
The grey wing upon every tide ;
For this that all that blood was shed,
For this Edward Fitzgerald died,
And Robert Emmet and Wolfe Tone,
All that delirium of the brave ?
Romantic Ireland's dead and gone,
It's with O'Leary in the grave.

Yet could we turn the years again,
And call those exiles as they were
In all their loneliness and pain,
You'd cry, 'Some woman's yellow hair
Has maddened every mother's son':
They weighed so lightly what they gave.
But let them be, they're dead and gone,
They're with O'Leary in the grave.

Running to Paradise

As I came over Windy Gap
They threw a halfpenny into my cap,
For I am running to Paradise ;
And all that I need do is to wish
And somebody puts his hand in the dish
To throw me a bit of salted fish :
And there the king is but as the beggar.

My brother Mourteen is worn out
With skelping his big brawling lout,
And I am running to Paradise ;
A poor life, do what he can,
And though he keep a dog and a gun,
A serving-maid and a serving-man :
And there the king is but as the beggar.

Poor men have grown to be rich men,
And rich men grown to be poor again,
And I am running to Paradise ;
And many a darling wit's grown dull
That tossed a bare heel when at school,
Now it has filled an old sock full :
And there the king is but as the beggar.

The wind is old and still at play
While I must hurry upon my way,
For I am running to Paradise ;
Yet never have I lit on a friend
To take my fancy like the wind
That nobody can buy or bind :
And there the king is but as the beggar.

I

To a Child Dancing in the Wind

DANCE there upon the shore ;
What need have you to care
For wind or water's roar ?
And tumble out your hair
That the salt drops have wet ;
Being young you have not known
The fool's triumph, nor yet
Love lost as soon as won,
Nor the best labourer dead
And all the sheaves to bind.
What need have you to dread
The monstrous crying of wind ?

Two Years Later

HAS no one said those daring
Kind eyes should be more learn'd ?
Or warned you how despairing
The moths are when they are burned ?
I could have warned you ; but you are young,
So we speak a different tongue.

O you will take whatever's offered
And dream that all the world's a friend,
Suffer as your mother suffered,
Be as broken in the end.
But I am old and you are young,
And I speak a barbarous tongue.

An Appointment

BEING out of heart with government
I took a broken root to fling
Where the proud, wayward squirrel went,
Taking delight that he could spring ;
And he, with that low whinnying sound
That is like laughter, sprang again
And so to the other tree at a bound.
Nor the tame will, nor timid brain,
Nor heavy knitting of the brow
Bred that fierce tooth and cleanly limb
And threw him up to laugh on the bough ;
No government appointed him.

A Coat

I MADE my song a coat
Covered with embroideries
Out of old mythologies
From heel to throat ;
But the fools caught it,
Wore it in the world's eyes
As though they'd wrought it.
Song, let them take it,
For there's more enterprise
In walking naked.

The Wild Swans at Coole

THE trees are in their autumn beauty,
The woodland paths are dry,
Under the October twilight the water
Mirrors a still sky ;
Upon the brimming water among the stones
Are nine-and-fifty swans.

The nineteenth autumn has come upon me
Since I first made my count ;
I saw, before I had well finished,
All suddenly mount
And scatter wheeling in great broken rings
Upon their clamorous wings.

I have looked upon those brilliant creatures,
And now my heart is sore.
All's changed since I, hearing at twilight,
The first time on this shore,
The bell-beat of their wings above my head,
Trod with a lighter tread.

Unwearied still, lover by lover,
They paddle in the cold
Companionable streams or climb the air ;
Their hearts have not grown old ;
Passion or conquest, wander where they will,
Attend upon them still.

But now they drift on the still water,
Mysterious, beautiful ;
Among what rushes will they build,
By what lake's edge or pool
Delight men's eyes when I awake some day
To find they have flown away ?

An Irish Airman Foresees his Death

I KNOW that I shall meet my fate
Somewhere among the clouds above ;
Those that I fight I do not hate,
Those that I guard I do not love ;
My country is Kiltartan Cross,
My countrymen Kiltartan's poor,
No likely end could bring them loss
Or leave them happier than before.
Nor law, nor duty bade me fight,
Nor public men, nor cheering crowds,
A lonely impulse of delight
Drove to this tumult in the clouds ;
I balanced all, brought all to mind,
The years to come seemed waste of breath,
A waste of breath the years behind
In balance with this life, this death.

A Song

I THOUGHT no more was needed
Youth to prolong
Than dumb-bell and foil
To keep the body young.
O who could have foretold
That the heart grows old?

Though I have many words,
What woman's satisfied,
I am no longer faint
Because at her side?
O who could have foretold
That the heart grows old?

I have not lost desire
But the heart that I had;
I thought 'twould burn my body
Laid on the death-bed,
For who could have foretold
That the heart grows old?

The Scholars

BALD heads forgetful of their sins,
Old, learned, respectable bald heads
Edit and annotate the lines
That young men, tossing on their beds,
Rhymed out in love's despair
To flatter beauty's ignorant ear.

All shuffle there ; all cough in ink ;
All wear the carpet with their shoes ;
All think what other people think ;
All know the man their neighbour knows.
Lord, what would they say
Did their Catullus walk that way ?

The Fisherman

ALTHOUGH I can see him still,
The freckled man who goes
To a grey place on a hill
In grey Connemara clothes
At dawn to cast his flies,
It's long since I began
To call up to the eyes
This wise and simple man.
All day I'd looked in the face
What I had hoped 'twould be
To write for my own race
And the reality ;
The living men that I hate,
The dead man that I loved,
The craven man in his seat,
The insolent unreproved,
And no knave brought to book
Who has won a drunken cheer,
The witty man and his joke
Aimed at the commonest ear,
The clever man who cries
The catch-cries of the clown,
The beating down of the wise
And great Art beaten down.

Maybe a twelvemonth since
Suddenly I began,

In scorn of this audience,
Imagining a man,
And his sun-freckled face,
And grey Connemara cloth,
Climbing up to a place
Where stone is dark under froth,
And the down-turn of his wrist
When the flies drop in the stream ;
A man who does not exist,
A man who is but a dream ;
And cried, 'Before I am old
I shall have written him one
Poem maybe as cold
And passionate as the dawn.'

Memory

ONE had a lovely face,
And two or three had charm,
But charm and face were in vain
Because the mountain grass
Cannot but keep the form
Where the mountain hare has lain.

The Cat and the Moon

THE cat went here and there
And the moon spun round like a top,
And the nearest kin of the moon,
The creeping cat, looked up.
Black Minnaloushe stared at the moon,
For, wander and wail as he would,
The pure cold light in the sky
Troubled his animal blood.
Minnaloushe runs in the grass
Lifting his delicate feet.
Do you dance, Minnaloushe, do you dance?
When two close kindred meet,
What better than call a dance?
Maybe the moon may learn,

Tired of that courtly fashion,
A new dance turn.
Minnaloushe creeps through the grass
From moonlit place to place,
The sacred moon overhead
Has taken a new phase.
Does Minnaloushe know that his pupils
Will pass from change to change,
And that from round to crescent,
From crescent to round they range?
Minnaloushe creeps through the grass
Alone, important and wise,
And lifts to the changing moon
His changing eyes.

The Rose Tree

'O WORDS are lightly spoken,'
Said Pearse to Connolly,
'Maybe a breath of politic words
Has withered our Rose Tree ;
Or maybe but a wind that blows
Across the bitter sea.'

'It needs to be but watered,'
James Connolly replied,
'To make the green come out again
And spread on every side,
And shake the blossom from the bud
To be the garden's pride.'

'But where can we draw water,'
Said Pearse to Connolly,
'When all the wells are parched away ?
O plain as plain can be
There's nothing but our own red blood
Can make a right Rose Tree.'

To be Carved on a Stone at Thoor Ballylee

I, THE poet William Yeats,
With old mill boards and sea-green slates,
And smith work from the Gort forge,
Restored this tower for my wife George ;
And may these characters remain
When all is ruin once again.

For Anne Gregory

'NEVER shall a young man,
Thrown into despair
By those great honey-coloured
Ramparts at your ear,
Love you for yourself alone
And not your yellow hair.'

'But I can get a hair-dye
And set such colour there,
Brown, or black, or carrot,
That young men in despair
May love me for myself alone
And not my yellow hair.'

'I heard an old religious man
But yesternight declare
That he had found a text to prove
That only God, my dear,
Could love you for yourself alone
And not your yellow hair.'

A Prayer for Old Age

GOD guard me from those thoughts men think
In the mind alone ;
He that sings a lasting song
Thinks in a marrow-bone ;

From all that makes a wise old man
That can be praised of all ;
O what am I that I should not seem
For the song's sake a fool ?

I pray — for fashion's word is out
And prayer comes round again —
That I may seem, though I die old,
A foolish, passionate man.

The Wicked Hawthorn Tree

First Attendant.   O, but I saw a solemn sight ;
  Said the rambling, shambling travelling-man ;
  Castle Dargan's ruin all lit,
  Lovely ladies dancing in it.

Second Attendant.   What though they danced !   Those
    days are gone,
  Said the wicked, crooked, hawthorn tree ;
  Lovely lady or gallant man
  Are blown cold dust or a bit of bone.

First Attendant.   O, what is life but a mouthful of air ?
  Said the rambling, shambling travelling-man ;
  Yet all the lovely things that were
  Live, for I saw them dancing there.

Second Attendant.   Nobody knows what may befall,
  Said the wicked, crooked, hawthorn tree.
  I have stood so long by a gap in the wall
  Maybe I shall not die at all.

From *Supernatural Songs*
IX
The Four Ages of Man

HE with body waged a fight,
But body won ; it walks upright.

Then he struggled with the heart ;
Innocence and peace depart.

Then he struggled with the mind ;
His proud heart he left behind.

Now his wars on God begin ;
At stroke of midnight God shall win.

What Then?

His chosen comrades thought at school
He must grow a famous man ;
He thought the same and lived by rule,
All his twenties crammed with toil ;
'*What then ?*' *sang Plato's ghost.* '*What then ?*'

Everything he wrote was read,
After certain years he won
Sufficient money for his need,
Friends that have been friends indeed ;
'*What then ?*' *sang Plato's ghost.* '*What then ?*'

All his happier dreams came true —
A small old house, wife, daughter, son,

Grounds where plum and cabbage grew,
Poets and Wits about him drew ;
'What then?' sang Plato's ghost. 'What then?'

'The work is done,' grown old he thought,
'According to my boyish plan ;
Let the fools rage, I swerved in naught,
Something to perfection brought' ;
But louder sang that ghost, 'What then?'

The Ghost of Roger Casement

O WHAT has made that sudden noise ?
What on the threshold stands ?
It never crossed the sea because
John Bull and the sea are friends ;
But this is not the old sea
Nor this the old seashore.
What gave that roar of mockery,
That roar in the sea's roar ?
The ghost of Roger Casement
Is beating on the door.

John Bull has stood for Parliament,
A dog must have his day,
The country thinks no end of him,
For he knows how to say,
At a beanfeast or a banquet,
That all must hang their trust
Upon the British Empire,
Upon the Church of Christ.
The ghost of Roger Casement
Is beating on the door.

John Bull has gone to India
And all must pay him heed,
For histories are there to prove
That none of another breed
Has had a like inheritance,

Or sucked such milk as he,
And there's no luck about a house
If it lack honesty.
The ghost of Roger Casement
Is beating on the door.

I poked about a village church
And found his family tomb
And copied out what I could read
In that religious gloom ;
Found many a famous man there ;
But fame and virtue rot.
Draw round, beloved and bitter men,
Draw round and raise a shout ;
The ghost of Roger Casement
Is beating on the door.

Come Gather Round Me, Parnellites

COME gather round me, Parnellites,
And praise our chosen man ;
Stand upright on your legs awhile,
Stand upright while you can,
For soon we lie where he is laid,
And he is underground ;
Come fill up all those glasses
And pass the bottle round.

And here's a cogent reason,
And I have many more,
He fought the might of England
And saved the Irish poor,
Whatever good a farmer's got
He brought it all to pass ;
And here's another reason,
That Parnell loved a lass.

And here's a final reason,
He was of such a kind
Every man that sings a song
Keeps Parnell in his mind.
For Parnell was a proud man,
No prouder trod the ground,
And a proud man's a lovely man,
So pass the bottle round.

The Bishops and the Party
That tragic story made,
A husband that had sold his wife
And after that betrayed ;
But stories that live longest
Are sung above the glass,
And Parnell loved his country,
And Parnell loved his lass.

Three Songs to the One Burden

III

Come gather round me, players all :
Come praise Nineteen-Sixteen,
Those from the pit and gallery
Or from the painted scene
That fought in the Post Office
Or round the City Hall,
Praise every man that came again,
Praise every man that fell.
From mountain to mountain ride the fierce horsemen.

Who was the first man shot that day ?
The player Connolly,
Close to the City Hall he died ;

Carriage and voice had he ;
He lacked those years that go with skill,
But later might have been
A famous, a brilliant figure
Before the painted scene.
From mountain to mountain ride the fierce horsemen.

Some had no thought of victory
But had gone out to die
That Ireland's mind be greater,
Her heart mount up on high ;
And yet who knows what's yet to come ?
For Patrick Pearse had said
That in every generation
Must Ireland's blood be shed.
From mountain to mountain ride the fierce horsemen.

Why should not Old Men be Mad?

WHY should not old men be mad?
Some have known a likely lad
That had a sound fly-fisher's wrist
Turn to a drunken journalist;
A girl that knew all Dante once
Live to bear children to a dunce;
A Helen of social welfare dream,
Climb on a wagonette to scream.
Some think it a matter of course that chance
Should starve good men and bad advance,
That if their neighbours figured plain,
As though upon a lighted screen,
No single story would they find
Of an unbroken happy mind,
A finish worthy of the start.
Young men know nothing of this sort,
Observant old men know it well;
And when they know what old books tell,
And that no better can be had,
Know why an old man should be mad.

The Statesman's Holiday

I LIVED among great houses,
Riches drove out rank,
Base drove out the better blood,
And mind and body shrank.
No Oscar ruled the table,
But I'd a troop of friends
That knowing better talk had gone
Talked of odds and ends.
Some knew what ailed the world
But never said a thing,
So I have picked a better trade
And night and morning sing :
Tall dames go walking in grass-green Avalon.

Am I a great Lord Chancellor
That slept upon the Sack?
Commanding officer that tore
The khaki from his back?
Or am I de Valéra,
Or the King of Greece,
Or the man that made the motors?
Ach, call me what you please!
Here's a Montenegrin lute,
And its old sole string
Makes me sweet music
And I delight to sing:
Tall dames go walking in grass-green Avalon.

With boys and girls about him,
With any sort of clothes,
With a hat out of fashion,
With old patched shoes,
With a ragged bandit cloak,
With an eye like a hawk,
With a stiff straight back,
With a strutting turkey walk,
With a bag full of pennies,
With a monkey on a chain,
With a great cock's feather,
With an old foul tune.
Tall dames go walking in grass-green Avalon.

Politics

How can I, that girl standing there,
My attention fix
On Roman or on Russian
Or on Spanish politics ?
Yet here's a travelled man that knows
What he talks about,
And there's a politician
That has read and thought,
And maybe what they say is true
Of war and war's alarms,
But O that I were young again
And held her in my arms !

From *Under Ben Bulben*

V

IRISH poets, learn your trade,
Sing whatever is well made,
Scorn the sort now growing up
All out of shape from toe to top,
Their unremembering hearts and heads
Base-born products of base beds.
Sing the peasantry, and then
Hard-riding country gentlemen,
The holiness of monks, and after
Porter-drinkers' randy laughter ;
Sing the lords and ladies gay
That were beaten into the clay
Through seven heroic centuries ;
Cast your mind on other days
That we in coming days may be
Still the indomitable Irishry.

VI

Under bare Ben Bulben's head
In Drumcliff churchyard Yeats is laid.
An ancestor was rector there
Long years ago, a church stands near,
By the road an ancient cross.
No marble, no conventional phrase ;
On limestone quarried near the spot

By his command these words are cut :

> *Cast a cold eye*
> *On life, on death.*
> *Horseman, pass by !*

Index of First Lines

All things uncomely and broken, all things worn out and old   37

Although I can see him still   69

As I came over Windy Gap   56

Bald heads forgetful of their sins   68

Being out of heart with government   61

Come gather round me, Parnellites   83

Come gather round me, players all   85

Dance there upon the shore   59

God guard me from those thoughts men think   76

Had I the heavens' embroidered cloths   46

Has no one said those daring   59

He with body waged a fight   78

His chosen comrades thought at school   79

How can I, that girl standing there   90

I heard the old, old men say   52

I know that I shall meet my fate   66

I lived among great houses   88

I made my song a coat   62

I passed along the water's edge below the humid trees   27

I rise in the dawn, and I kneel and blow   42

I, the poet William Yeats   74

I thought no more was needed   67

I went out to the hazel wood   41

I whispered, 'I am too young'   53

I will arise and go now, and go to Innisfree   33

Irish poets, learn your trade   91

'Never shall a young man   75

O, but I saw a solemn sight   77
O what has made that sudden noise?   81
'O words are lightly spoken'   73
O'Driscoll drove with a song   38
One had a lovely face   71

Shy one, shy one   31

The cat went here and there   71
The jester walked in the garden   44
The old brown thorn-trees break in two high over Cummen
    Strand   51
The old priest Peter Gilligan   35
The trees are in their autumn beauty   63

Under bare Ben Bulben's head   91

We sat together at one summer's end   48
We who are old, old and gay   32
What need you, being come to sense   54
When I play on my fiddle in Dooney   47
When my arms wrap you round I press   43
When you are old and grey and full of sleep   34
Where dips the rocky highland   28
Why should not old men be mad?   87

You say, as I have often given tongue   53